ULTIMATE X-MEN

ULTIMATE COLLECTION

Writers
Mark Millar
with **Chuck Austen** (Issues #13-14)

Art (Issues #15-17, #20-22 & #25)
Pencils: **Adam Kubert**
Inks: **Danny Miki**
Colors: **Dave Stewart** with **J.D. Smith and Chris Sotomayor**

Art (Issues #13-14)
Pencils: **Esad Ribic**
Inks: **Livesay**
Colors: **J.D. Smith**

Art (Issues #18-19)
Artist: **Chris Bachalo**
Colors: **Dave Stewart**

Art (Issues #23-24)
Artist: **Kaare Andrews**
Digital Paints: **Dave McCaig & Chris Sotomayor**

Letters: **Chris Eliopoulos** with **Sharpefont** (Issues #13-14)
Cover Art: **Adam Kubert & Richard Isanove**
Assistant Editor: **Pete Franco**
Associate Editors: **C.B. Cebulski & Brian Smith**
Editors: **Ralph Macchio & Mark Powers**

Collection Editor: **Jennifer Grünwald**
Assistant Editors: **Cory Levine & Michael Short**
Associate Editor: **Mark D. Beazley**
Senior Editor, Special Projects: **Jeff Youngquist**
Senior Vice President of Sales: **David Gabriel**
Vice President of Creative: **Tom Marvelli**

Editor in Chief: **Joe Quesada**
Publisher: **Dan Buckley**

PREVIOUSLY

They are the X-Men — sworn to protect a world that fears and hates them. Led by Professor Charles Xavier, young mutants Cyclops, Marvel Girl, Wolverine, Storm, Beast, Colossus and Iceman use their mutant abilities for the betterment of mankind as a whole.

Weapon X, the covert government project that turned mutants into living weapons, is no more. Despite their capture, the X-Men helped bring it down and have once again regrouped at the X-Mansion in New York's Westchester County. As headmaster of the School for Gifted Youngsters, Professor X was pleased with the performance of his students, and now things are quiet at the academy.

But not all mutants have been fortunate enough to be rescued by Charles Xavier. Some must survive by their wits alone, with nobody to whom they can turn. Each day, they face the scorn and fear of the human world — and sometimes, of themselves.

One such mutant is Remy LeBeau, who is about to learn he's not nearly as untouchable as he likes to believe...

YOU ALWAYS REMEMBER YOUR FIRST LOVE
PART I

Allan Silvermane Enterprises.

Yes, sir.

They claim the package was delivered first thing this morning. They're checking on the signature.

Um-- excuse me?

Can I help you?

No.

But somebody better!!

It Doesn't Have to be This Way

According to the Oxford English Dictionary, it's an individual, organism or new genetic character arising or resulting from MUTATION.

According to the NEWSPAPERS, it's a super-powered sociopath hell-bent on nothing less than the ABSOLUTE DESTRUCTION of the entire HUMAN RACE.

The truth, like MOST things, lies somewhere in the MIDDLE.

My OWN definition of that six-letter word is just an ORDINARY PERSON with an EXTRAORDINARY TALENT.

WHY we have these gifts is impossible to say.

Speculation ranges from holes in the OZONE LAYER to nature preparing us for life in the THIRD MILLENNIUM, but no one REALLY knows the answer.

All we know is that these talents make us DIFFERENT and those differences make people NERVOUS in these STRANGE, UNCERTAIN TIMES.

My name is Professor Charles Xavier and as I prepare for an international tour to promote a BOOK I've just published, I've been asked to write an article which might ALLEVIATE your fears.

W'Micro...

File   Edit
View   Insert
Format   Tools
Table   Window
Help

Normal

I want to tell you about a SCHOOL I founded where these EXTRAORDINARY TALENTS are being very carefully CULTIVATED.

3500   DELL

Personally, I've never understood why individuals who exhibit MUTANT abilities are regarded with suspicion when every other form of excellence is LAUDED by society.

Are songwriters persecuted for the power of their LYRICS? Are Quarterbacks hounded for the accuracy of their ARMS?

Miss this and you don't get near me for a *week*, McCoy.

I am truly *sorry* about this, Henry, my friend.

Don't worry about it, Peter. I've

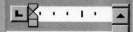

Of course, I don't mean to diminish the BIOLOGY of the situation when ninety-eight percent of all known mutants test positive for the X-FACTOR gene...

But aren't we all slaves to our inherited genetics?

After all, some say MUSIC runs in families...

...and others are clearly born with an aptitude for SPORT.

Are mutants SINGLED OUT for alienation because our talents can extend to FREEZING RAIN-DROPS and LEVELING MOUNTAINS?

Is our world-shaking POTENTIAL the reason young mutant teenagers only dare communicate through INTERNET CHAT ROOMS?

Dear reader, as I argue at length in my book, this RAW POWER you fear is precisely the reason that these young, terrified mutants must be EMBRACED.

Can't you imagine their potential for GOOD with the proper GUIDANCE and TEACHING?

Marvel Girl is a PERFECT EXAMPLE.

When I found her, those formidable psychic powers were so unfocused that she was unable to distinguish between VOICES and THOUGHTS.

Through careful training, her abilities were SUPPRESSED, and now, over time, are being gradually REINTRODUCED.

Her main area of school work is dealing with the MENTALLY-ILL, but she's been helping police find three missing persons lately, and is reportedly making excellent progress.

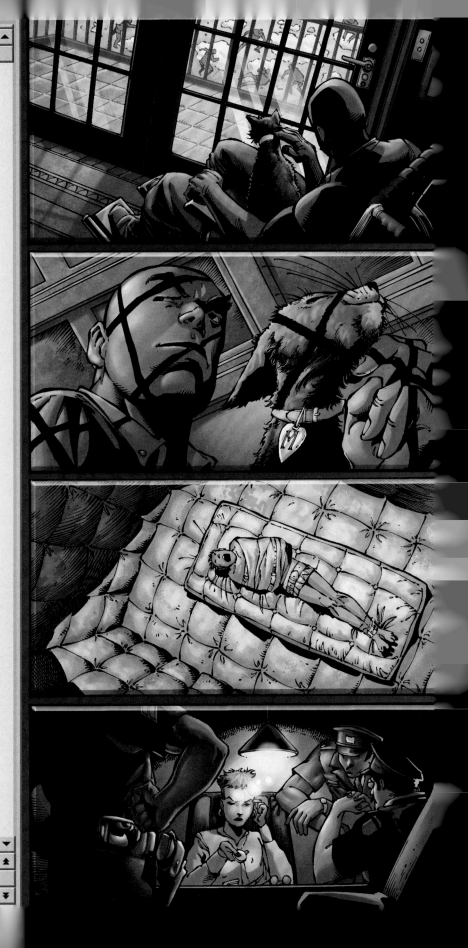

Storm is ANOTHER young student who has blossomed in the short time she's been following my PROGRAM.

An illegal Moroccan immigrant with almost no formal schooling, she's currently in the middle of a telepathic JOINT-DIPLOMA in both HORTICULTURE and ECONOMICS.

Last week, she used her atmospheric manipulation to reinvigorate a recession-hit FARMING COMMMUNITY and achieved a well-deserved A-PLUS for APPLIED USE of her ABILITIES.

Of course, there's more to education than TRADITIONAL ACADEMICS. My syllabus specializes in pop-culture, conversation and the arts of SELF-DEFENSE too.

Cyclops, for example, might have very poor grades, but his leadership skills are EXCEPTIONAL in our virtual reality COMBAT CLASSES.

Twice a week, between CHEMISTRY and HUMOR, I ask him to utilize these gifts and do something DANGEROUS with groups of UNDER-PRIVILEGED YOUNGSTERS.

As a orphan HIMSELF, I know he appreciates the importance of a solid and dependable ROLE MODEL.

When we first found him, ICEMAN was as traumatized and frightened as any OTHER fifteen-year-old schoolboy would be in his unusual situation…

But his warm heart and sense of humor have been a source of strength to EVERYONE lately; particularly in the late-night COMPASSION EXERCISES I assigned him.

The same holds true for our sensitive and intelligent BEAST. More than ANYONE, he has a right to despise mankind for the atrocities which were committed against him.

But his passion for RESEARCH remains undiminished, his latest project being a breathtaking alternative to the expensive pharmaceuticals required in THIRD WORLD COUNTRIES…

…although, I must confess, I DO worry about the amount of time my prize student spends working in the SCHOOL LABORATORY sometimes.

But perhaps the development I'm MOST proud of is how WOLVERINE and COLOSSUS have reinvented themselves over these last few months.

Both young men raised in violence and misery, they now spend their evenings scanning newspapers for HARD-LUCK STORIES and UNSOLVED CRIMES…

…walking the streets from dusk 'til dawn in search of people who might need their PARTICULAR kind of HELP.

Of course, it would be NAÏVE to suggest that the MUTANT INFLUENCE is always an ENTIRELY positive one.

It's understandable that people are afraid when they see their homo-sapien children declare themselves X-FACTOR POSITIVE or hear the lyrics to their ANTI-HUMAN SONGS.

Spike Lee's upcoming MAGNETO bio-pic clearly isn't going to help matters, nor is Professor Bolivar Trask's popular theory that mutants have cruelty HARD-WIRED into our GENES.

It's a VERY COMPELLING ARGUMENT…

…particularly in light of The Brotherhood of Mutants' re-emergence as a political force and what they did to the Japanese FINANCIAL DISTRICT last week.

My students and I might have neutralized MAGNETO back in Washington, but I'm afraid his children inherited more than just their father's striking EASTERN EUROPEAN PROFILE.

I think you might find Cyclops is considering a move back to *our* side soon, Uncle Charles. Did you know he and Toad had a four hour *telephone conversation* last night?

Yes, but they were talking about *The Lord of the Rings*, Quicksilver. Besides, why would he be interested in rejoining The Brotherhood when you've so clearly lost your *way* lately?

I'd hardly describe renewing our assault upon corrupt human *power-bases* as *losing our way*, sir.

In fact, the current state of confusion in the Western World should make replacing the *status quo* that much *easier* over the coming weeks and months.

And you think *bombing* the old order will make the human population embrace you as their *leaders*, Scarlet Witch?

Terrorism might have made sense in your *father's* world, but it's never been less fashionable than it is right now, my dear.

Some people ask why we don't just WAGE WAR on The Brotherhood, but that's such an old-fashioned, IMPERIALISTIC solution to the problem…

As we look around the world today, it's clear that violence breeds nothing but FURTHER violence.

IDEAS are the only way to change the world and, as a teacher, I feel it's my responsibility to PROVE it.

I've always thought it must take a very special kind of person to work with the *severely handicapped.*

Then again, they say the *teachers* gain as much from the experience as the *children.* What do *you* think, Peter?

I can't say I've really given the matter much *thought,* Professor.

Do you recognize the gentleman in the tan jacket playing with the little Down's Syndrome twins over there, young man?

Can you tell me where you might have seen his face *before?*

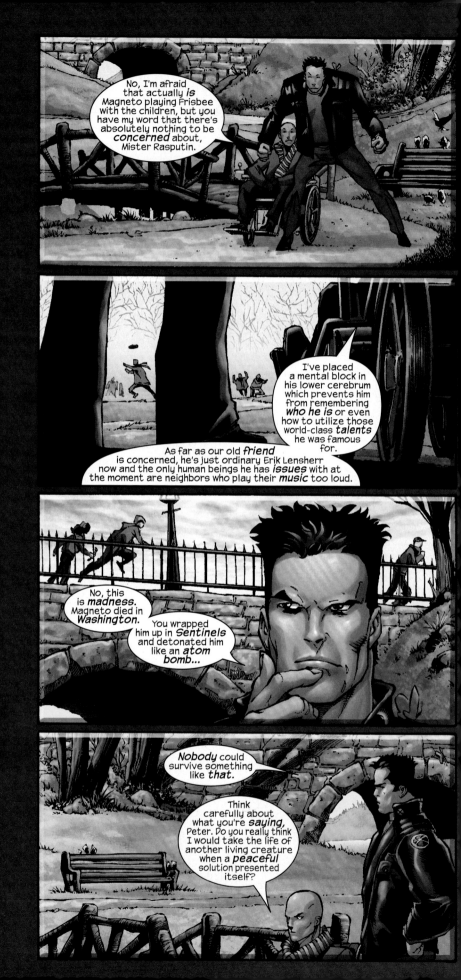

When I returned home this evening to have our picture taken, Wolverine asked if he could borrow one of my suits because he wanted to make a good impression in the magazine…

Cyclops was on the telephone to Toad, laughing about how Storm had caused a tiny thunderstorm in Iceman's large intestine for some reason. I must remember to ask about that later.

Shortly before I began to finish this article, the police called and said they had found the three missing girls precisely where Marvel Girl had suggested they LOOK for them.

For a moment, I pause and reflect upon Trask's idea and wonder if evolution is INDEED moving in the wrong direction.

But although man invented torture and cruelty, we must also remember that evolution gave us science and art and empathy as well as upright backs and opposable thumbs.

Why should people think we're just a mutation of everything BAD about themselves?

Isn't there a chance that we could also be an evolution of man's intrinsic capacity for GOOD?

ISSUE
X 16

Land's End, Scotland:

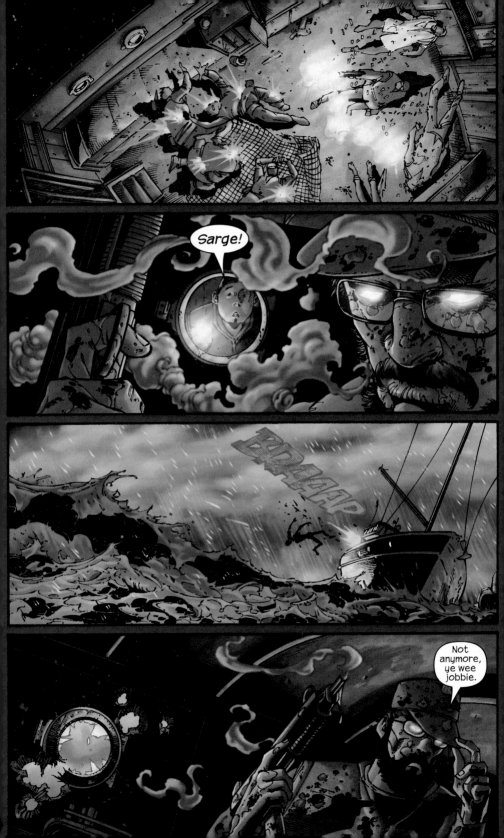

"Professor Xavier, on behalf of the audience, I'd just like to thank you for that inspirational lecture and open the floor up to the thousands of believers in the *audience*, sir.

"Is there anyone out there who'd like to ask the leader of the X-Men a *question?*"

"Hi, Professor. I was just curious how these X-Men operations are *funded*, sir. Is it true you use your psychic powers to manipulate *stocks* and *shares?*"

"No, the cars, the planes and my secret New York school are all paid for out of my *inheritance*, young man.

"It's true I play the *stock market*, but I'd never use my powers for anything as tawdry as *personal financial gain*."

"Did you really mean it when you said you don't have to be a *mutant* to be an X-Man?"

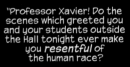

"Of course. The ideas outlined in the book are a manifesto for man and mutant-kind to live in *harmony*.

"An intelligent person doesn't have to be *x-factor positive* to put on a uniform and head out there to make a difference in their *neighborhood*."

"What about this rumor that there's a *second* school you've started, Professor Xavier? An island off the coast of *Europe* even your *pupils* don't know about?

"Is it true what they say on the Internet about a school where you're training less *socially acceptable* mutants?"

"I'm afraid I'm not in the *habit* of responding to *Internet speculation,* Miss. Next question, please."

"Professor Xavier! Do the scenes which greeted you and your students outside the Hall tonight ever make you *resentful* of the human race?"

"Professor?"

"I'm *sorry*, Professor. Should he repeat the question?"

"No, no. That won't be *necessary*.

"I teach my students the importance of turning the other cheek, but one can never get used to *hate*, young man.

"*Next question,* please."

Muir Island:

What can I *say*, Wolverine? David was just your typical, little *boy* when Charles and I were together-- average size, average intellect, a devoted *Glasgow Rangers* fan.

"Of course, we always *knew* he was carrying the X-gene, but his powers didn't actually manifest until the day after his father *left* and our lives were thrown into *turmoil*.

"As far as we could ascertain, David had a very limited control of the matter around his person, but even the *slightest* use of these abilities had a devastating effect on his physical body.

"My son would have been dead in a *week* if we hadn't kept him sedated on *Haloperidol* all these years and locked him in a lab where we could monitor him carefully.

"Why he started to convulse again last night, I still can't say, but I doubt it's a coincidence that his *father* was back in Britain with his nice, little *surrogate family*.

"Unfortunately, this convulsion turned out to be the *fatal* one and he'd have died right there on the operating table if he hadn't jumped into poor Isobel MacLinden."

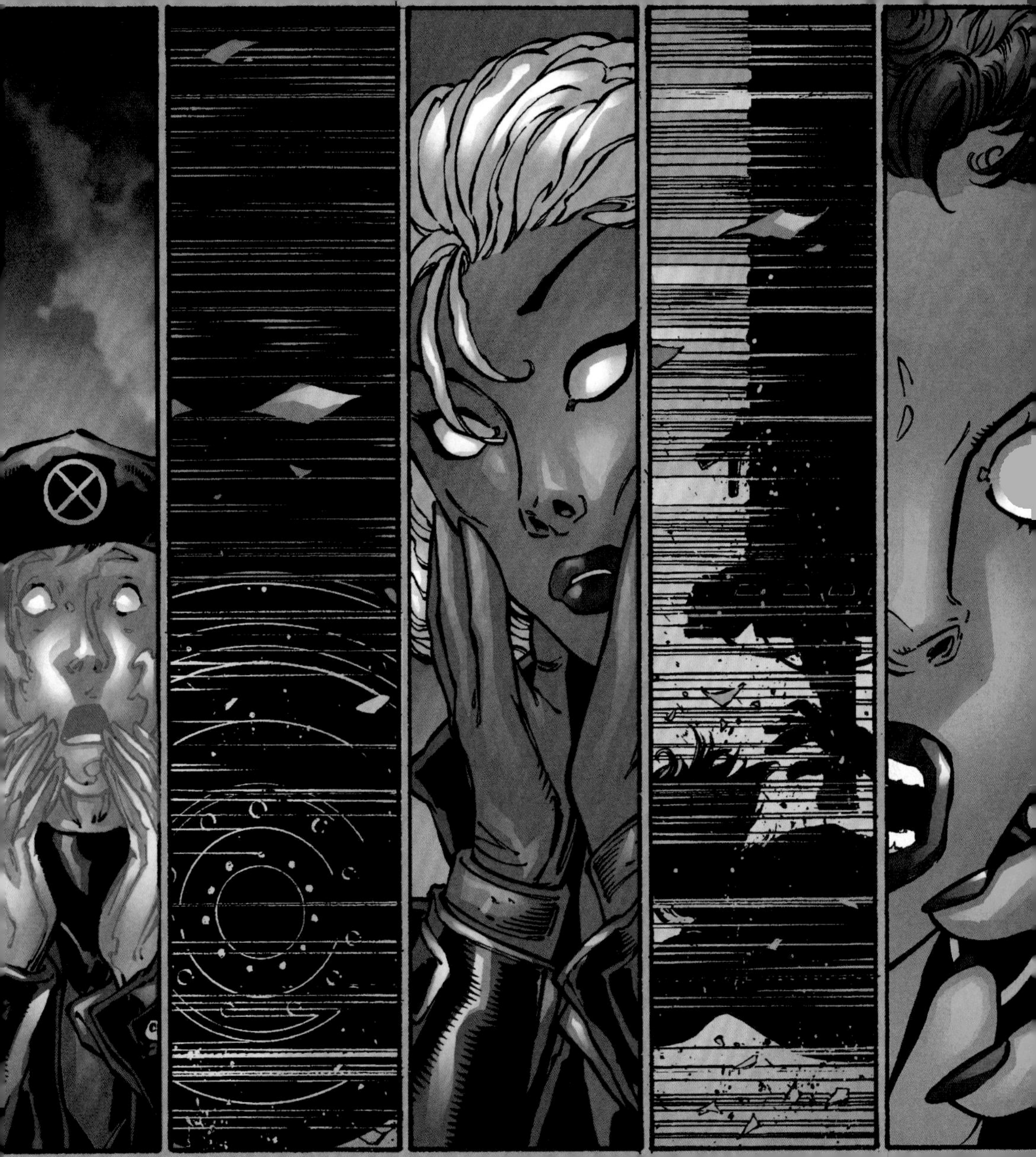

Do you really think it was a good idea heading to *Russia* right now, Jean? Suppose they're *needing* us back there?

Oh, don't be *silly*, Scott. So another teenager's having trouble with his *mutant abilities*. What's the worst that could *happen*?

Besides, the Professor and I both had the same gut feeling that finding Colossus was essential to whatever comes next and it's highly unlikely we're *both* off the mark, right?

I just hope he's got nothing to do with this *sub* going down near the *White Sea*. I'll *kill* him if he was behind this thing.

Going back to his old Russian Mob connections is *one* thing, but if this *submarine disaster* is some stupid stunt he's cooked up with *The Brotherhood*, I'm going to...

Hold that *thought*, Mister Summers.

That *psychic vapor trail* I've been following has just got so pungent I think I'm going to *gag*.

Colossus must be standing within a *half mile radius* of the car.

ISSUE
X 18

X-MEN:

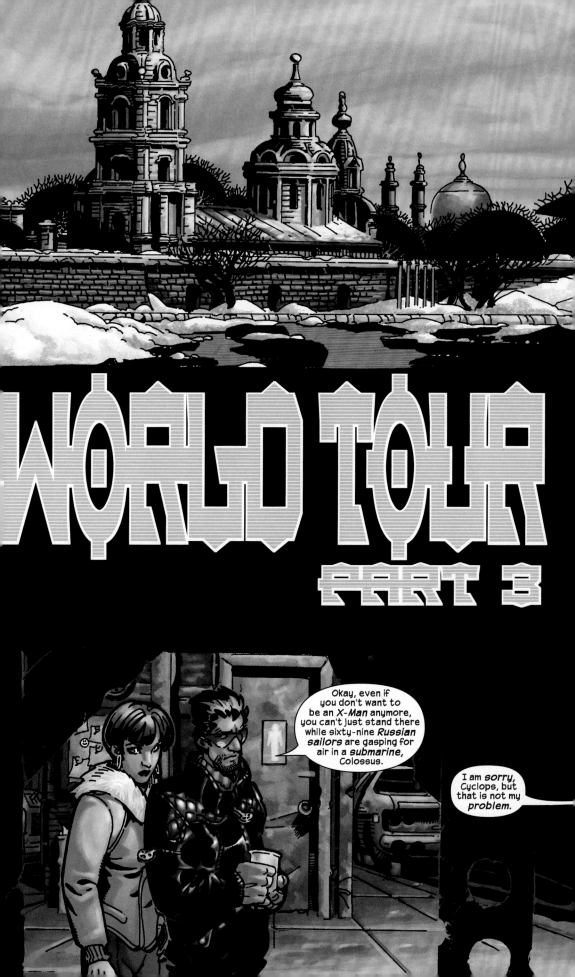

Ugh! I still can't believe we're chasing the Professor's *evil mutant son* instead of sunning ourselves on this *international book tour* we were promised.

Tell me about it, Storm. If I'd wanted to waste my time looking for fights with *certifiable nut-cases* I could have stayed in a *regular High School.*

Excuse me, Iceman, but David happens to be *my son too* and, as you very well know, suffers from a very serious *medical condition.*

Oh, sure. The kinda condition which makes him jump from *body to body* and kill as many folks as he can, right? Pardon me if I don't send *flowers,* Doctor MacTaggert.

Still, you gotta admit, it's pretty cool getting a military escort straight through the *airport,* Wolverine. Likewise, S.H.I.E.L.D. sending this new *super-team* to help us out.

The X-Men teaming up with *The Ultimates,* man. How spectacular is *this* going to be?

The only thing I don't understand is how this psychic *secret agent* chick can track this creep and Xavier *can't.*

Because he's been inside the Professor's *head* and designed a way of *blocking* him, Iceman. The lovely *Miss Braddock* over there's still an *unknown quantity.*

Not for much *longer,* by the looks of it. Betsy seems to be getting on pretty well with *the boss,* if you catch my drift.

Oh, psychics are *always* like that when they get together, Miss Munroe. It's actually a bit *creepy* watching them having those *silent* conversations.

Like watching people doing *sign-language* without moving their *hands*, you know?

What's *wrong*, Doctor? I thought you were *over* him?

It's only just occurred to me why David's lured everyone here to Germany. This is where Glasgow Rangers drew with Borrusia Dortmund in the European Cup back in 1995.

Dear God in Heaven.

This is where Charlie, David and I had our last *family* holiday.

Dublin Airport

Either that or she's got the *hots* for him, Inspector Thomas.

Oh, dear God, no!

I must admit, I'm a little surprised how shaken up Wolverine's been by all this, Professor. You always imagine someone with *his* reputation wouldn't be fazed by *anything*.

Well, Wolverine is a *feral beast*, Betsy.

He relies entirely on his senses and, for the first time in his life, he's up against an opponent where his abilities are essentially *useless*.

Tracking my son has been harrowing for everyone, but I'm confident that we'll capture and rehabilitate him soon-- especially with all this *super hero backup* you've arranged for us.

What do you mean *rehabilitate* him? You aren't planning to enlist this animal in your school, are you?

David's spent seven of the last nineteen years tied to a hospital bed, Betsy. He's probably the most powerful mutant in the world and he hasn't a *clue* how to use his powers.

Show me someone who needs a little education more than *he* does and I'll be very, very surprised, young lady.

You know, you're probably just about the strangest person I've ever met, but I'm really starting to *warm* to you, Professor.

Does it feel a bit weird being here with your ex-wife like this?

Not at all, actually. Moira MacTaggert and I *always* had a very complicated relationship.

Somehow, I just can't imagine you two being *married.*

Well, you'd be surprised. The two of us were very much *in love* for a great many *years.*

"We met when I was doing a post-graduate course in genetics at Glasgow University and got married three weeks later.

"Of course, mutants were still just a *rumor* in those days, but I knew what I was and, together with Moira, we pretty much wrote the book on *post-human medicine.*

"It was Moira who designed and built the big *Cerebro* prototype you saw up on Muir Island and we used this to track down any potential patients who might need our help.

"Boys made of *steam,* dogs made of *ice cream.* We tried to save them *all* through the nineteen-eighties.

"As you can imagine, it wasn't long before we attracted the attention of *another* forward-thinking individual with an interest in *mutant teenagers* too..."

"Magneto?"

"The very fellow."

"I don't know about you, but the first time I met another adult mutant was like being hit by a thunderbolt. Far, far more powerful than being in love and our human wives knew it.

"Our eyes were brighter. Our minds were faster. Sometimes we could spend seventy-two straight hours on the telephone just talking about our ideas for the world.

"Even poor, little *David* felt alienated when Magneto's twins would visit. This being, of course, several years before David's *own* mutant gene was activated.

"I honestly don't think there was one specific argument which *caused* me to leave.

"Just the drip-drip-drip of silent nights in front of the television set and the growing *unease* with my own child's *scent*.

"It's *monstrous* in *hindsight*, but I don't even think I said *goodbye* the night I left to build our little South Sea Island *Utopia*.

But, as everyone knows, Magneto and I had the most terrible *argument* when I discovered his plans, which left me crippled and confined to this *wheelchair*.

So, when my investors approached and offered to fund my secret New York school and this *second* home for *less fortunate* mutants, my thoughts drifted back to *Moira*.

You mean you hired her to assuage your *guilt* for walking out on your family a few years *before*?

Partially, but also because she's literally the best gene-woman in the business and because I wanted to make sure that my chronically-ill son had a comfortable home.

Do you ever feel *responsible* for David? I mean, the fact that his reality-warping powers kicked in the day after you *left*?

Not really. They were going to happen *anyway*, of course. What I *do* feel guilty about was not being there to guide him at an age when I think he needed me *most*.

I had no shortage of *love* for my son, you know.

Like an owner's love for his *pet*, sometimes, but it was *love nonetheless*, Betsy.

<Good evening, ladies and gentlemen. Welcome to Global News.>

<Time seems to be running out for the sailors trapped in the downed K-14 submarine in the Barent's Sea.>

<Where are these so-called heroes in our hour of need?>

It appears hopes of Iron Man's assistance have been dashed as Tony Stark seems to be occupied elsewhere.>

<Our hearts go out to the families of these brave sailors who don't know if their sons will ever be coming home again...>

Okay, Tony Stark might be stuck up in *space* right now, but you're going to have British, German and French divers backing you up *all the way* down there, mate.

If there's a *problem* and you really don't reckon you can dislodge the K-14, just give us the signal and we'll have you out of there in a *jiffy*, right?

There will not *be* a problem, Colonel...

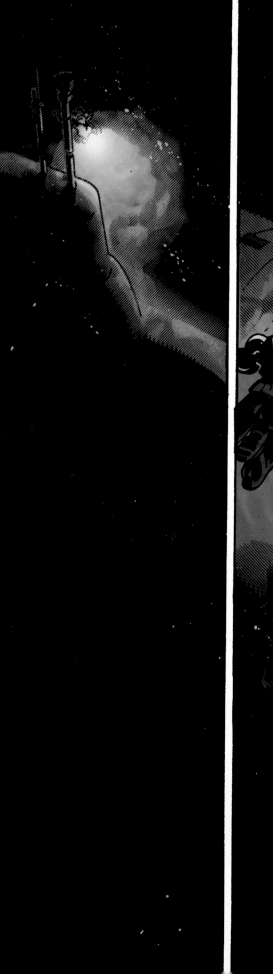

This is the BBC World Service with George Alagayah and the **news** **headlines** every *fifteen minutes*...

Progress in Russia as the K-14 submarine is saved from disaster!

Details are *sketchy* at the moment, but, two hours ago, the Russian news agency TASS recommended that all foreign news crews head to **Murmansk** for further developments...

How the heck should I know what it is? All I know is I'm not going there without a *photographer*, dude! Just finish your beer and *move!*

Oh, for the love of *God!*

Is this a *front page* or is this a *front page?*

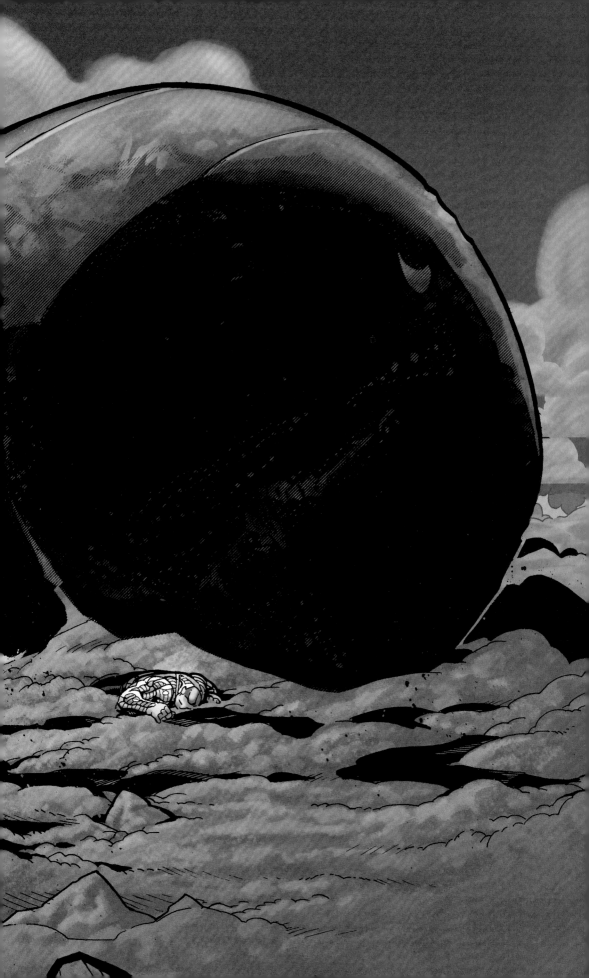

Boize Moi!

Well, how does it feel to suddenly find yourself the most famous super hero on the face of the *planet*, Colossus?

In all honesty?

Absolutely fabulous.

Did Moira go to pick up Colossus with the others, Professor?

No, she said she was heading back to the hotel to *lie down*, Betsy. She hasn't really been *herself* since that hip operation.

CARRBUCKS COFFEE

Berlin:
Do you ever wonder if the Professor screws around with our *minds* sometimes?
X-MEN:
What do you mean by *that,* Storm?
Well, look at *me,* for instance-- I'm a nasty, little witch with a *prison record* and yet here I am *en route* to the airport to give Colossus a great, big hug for coming back to the *team.*
I'm sorry, guys, but that just ain't *me.* Likewise, all this going up against *impossible odds* and chasing bad guys like the Professor's *evil mutant son* we're supposed to be hunting.
And yet I've never been more *committed* to anything in my *entire life.* What does *that* say to you, boys?
Do you think he's manipulating our *thoughts* and stuff like he does to keep *Magneto* in check?
Nah, no way.

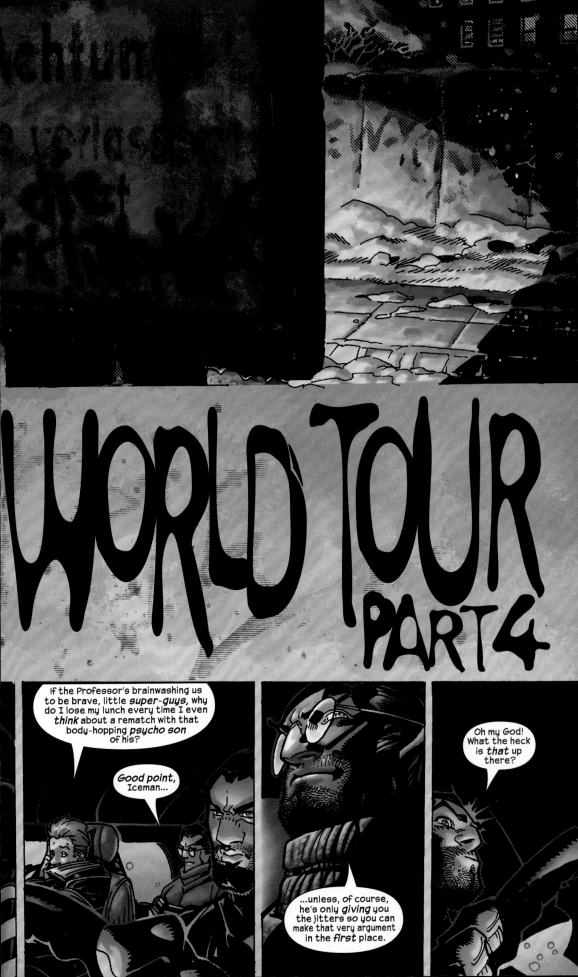

WORLD TOUR PART 4

If the Professor's brainwashing us to be brave, little *super-guys*, why do I lose my lunch every time I even *think* about a rematch with that body-hopping *psycho son* of his?

Good point, Iceman...

Oh my God! What the heck is *that* up there?

...unless, of course, he's only *giving* you the jitters so you can make that very argument in the *first* place.

C'mon, Dad. I might be using Betsy Braddock's powers to keep you out of *my* head, but you can still talk to your X-Men telepathically.

Tell them to put up a *fight*.

X-Men, this is *Xavier*. Regardless of what he's saying, David's still a *novice* with these reality-warping powers and our situation isn't as *desperate* as it *looks*.

Beast-- you're *fronting* the assault. Iceman and Storm-- I want a *power combination* like we practiced in class for the nine or ten minutes *Wolverine* needs to recover.

Suits me, folks. Just let me get a few seconds *on my own* with this cretin before you follow through with the *ice-storm*, okay?

What are you *waiting* for, Iceman? *Ice up!*

I *CAN'T!* I mean, I'm *trying*, but it's just not *working!* It's like my body doesn't wanna put me in a situation where it knows I'm gonna *die* or something!

What do we do *now*, Storm?

HANDS OFF THE HOTTIE!
ICEMAN!!
Was that a joke or was he really trying to be scary there?
You know, I wish you would have worried about me the way you worry about all these wee mutants of yours, Dad.
Would it make a difference now that I've got powers too? Could I start calling myself something cool like Proteus and maybe get a trial for that secret New York school of yours?
Where have you taken us, David?

Man that is born of a woman is of few days and full of trouble. He cometh forth like a flower, and is cut down; he fleeth also as a shadow, and continueth not.

Seeing his days are determined, the number of his months is with Thee; Thou hast appointed his bounds that he cannot pass; turn from him that he may rest, till he shall accomplish his day.

For there is hope of a tree, if it be cut down, that it will sprout again, and that the tender branch thereof will not cease.

But man dieth and wasteth away; yea, man giveth up the ghost, and where is he?

As the waters hail from the sea, and the flood decayeth and drieth up, so man lieth down, and riseth not till the heavens be no more.

Who said you've made a *mess* of things?

Oh, *come on.* David *dead,* the Braddock girl lying on a *mortuary slab,* poor little Bobby Drake fighting for his life in an *intensive care unit...*

His parents are taking him out of the school and suing me for *willful neglect.* They've told the press I'm a danger to *children* and I'm not sure I *disagree.*

How can I run a school to shape young minds when I couldn't even *raise David* properly? What kind of monster can't even cry at his own son's *funeral,* for God's sake?

You are *not a monster,* Charles.

No, I'm *careless* and *naive* and, frankly, that makes me even *more* dangerous these days.

The Auckland Sky-tower, New Zealand:

JEAN, I WANT A BUBBLE AROUND EVERYONE ON THE TEAM! STORM, TAKE OUT THE ACOLYTES!

Weschester County, New York:

The X-Men:

Professor X:

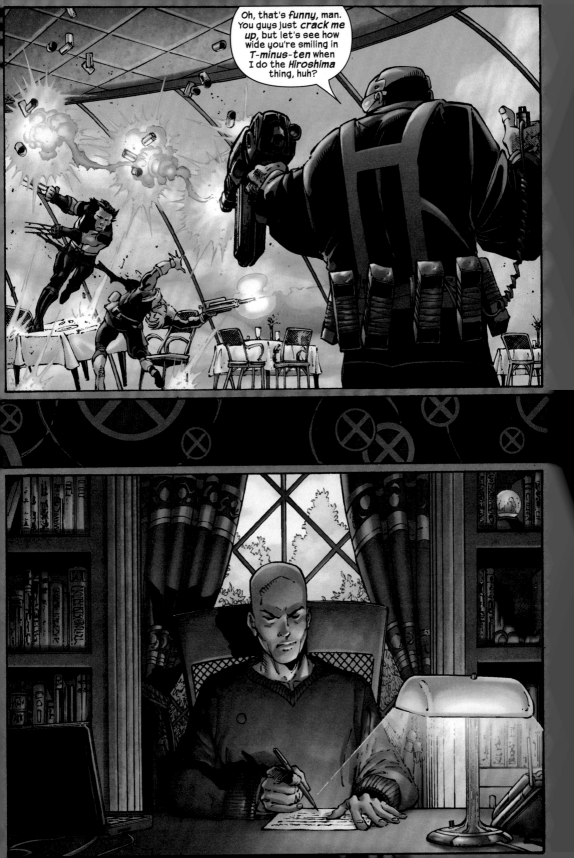

My dear Scott,

By the time you return from New Zealand, I will have packed my things and gone. I apologize for not saying this to your face, but you know how we telepaths are with verbal confrontation.

I'm leaving because I've FAILED... failed as a HUSBAND, failed as a FATHER and failed as a TEACHER.

My books and lectures told the world how man and mutant could live in HARMONY, but I realize now that I was WRONG.

Only ONE species may sit at the top of the food chain because that is the NATURAL ORDER of things.

I'm GLAD that my New York lecture was cancelled as a mark of respect for those David killed because I really couldn't spout my claptrap with Iceman lying in a HOSPITAL BED.

I'm GLAD new terror groups are beginning to form because what right did I have to subvert the ideals of THE BROTHERHOOD OF MUTANTS?

My BIGGEST conceit, however, was this psychic rehabilitation of MAGNETO I intended.

In retrospect, it's MIND-BOGGLING to think that I made a man forget who he was in the vague hope that he might one day come around to MY way of thinking.

MIND-BOGGLING.

That's why I plan to REMOVE those blocks later this afternoon.

It is clear to me now that Magneto must be freed and nature allowed to take her own course.

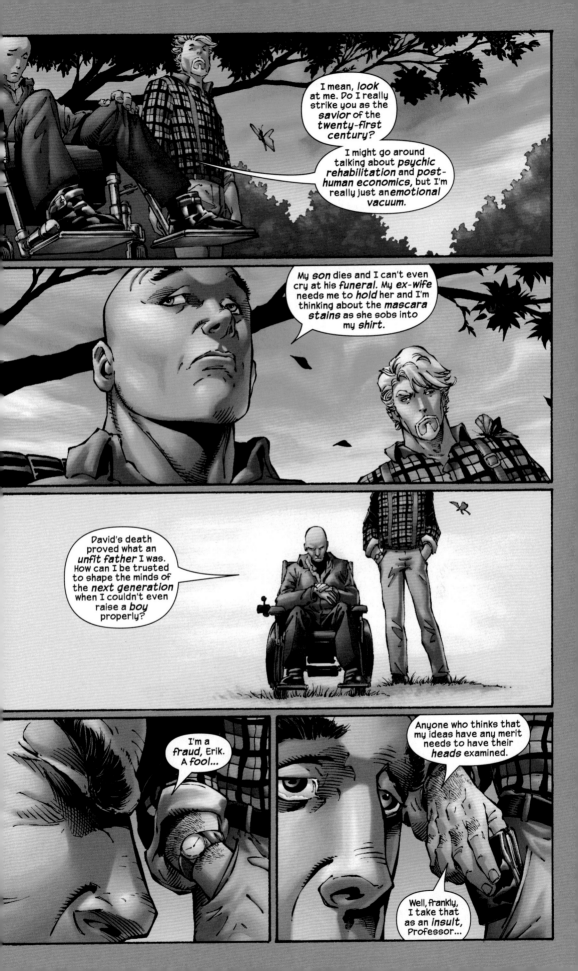

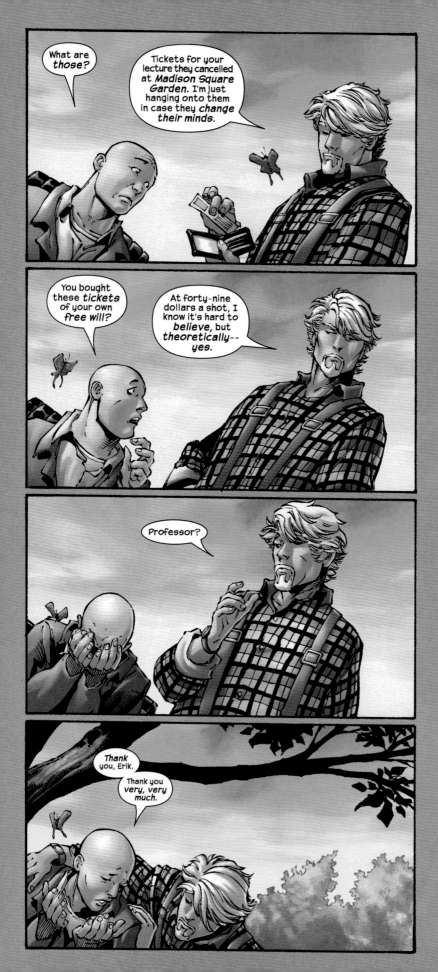

Are you absolutely sure these cops can't *see* us, Marvel Girl?

Oh, *please.* Sensory manipulation was one of the first things the Professor *taught* me, Cyclops.

As far as *New York's Finest* are concerned, we're just a couple of flies buzzing around against the *glass.*

It's horrible to think that's *Bobby* lying there, isn't it? He looks like a little broken *toy* or something.

How did things get this *screwed up,* Jean? How did we end up in a situation where the city is hiring *armed guards* to stop *The X-Men* visiting *Iceman?*

Because the Professor put him up against the most powerful mutant in the world when every *other* kid his age was playing *Metal Gear Solid,* Scott.

Bobby's Mom and Dad just did what *any* parent would do under the circumstances.

From: Charlesxavier@x-r
To: Theresapryde@ya
Subject: re: Help my daughter

Dear Mrs Pryde:
Thank you for the e-mail re
your daughter's recent
problems. Yes, I think o
could help Kitty a great
and propose we set up
at your earliest conveni
Please forward your groun
and I will ask Marvel Girl
arrange the necessary t
Yours sincerely,
Professor Charles Xavie

Dear Mrs. Pryde:
Thank you for the e-mail regarding your daughter's recent health
    problems. Yes, I think our school could help Kitty a great deal
    and propose we set up a meeting at your earliest convenience.
Please forward your ground address and I will ask Marvel Girl to
    arrange the necessary transport.
Yours sincerely,
    Professor Charles Xavier

Colossus and *Wolverine* over there are just home from a joint effort with the NYPD to bust an illegal street-drug derivative of some poor telepath's *cranial fluid.*

Judging by the bright, happy aura around *Peter* at the moment, I'd hazard a guess that it all went *pretty well* too.

Are you *nuts?* Wolverine's been shot to *pieces.*

Oh, do not worry about these little *bullet holes,* my friend.

His *healing factor* has already restored all his major organs and he should be *fighting fit* again by the time we are scheduled for our *Danger Room* exercises.

Danger Room?

Our *training arena,* Kitty. Just imagine your old *high school gym* rigged-up with every deathtrap you can *think* of and you're pretty much *halfway there.*

We used to use a *virtual reality* version, but the *program* kept crashing. I think the *tangible* one works better, *anyway.*

Who's in *here?* Another *cute guy?*

Oh, that's our *resident genius.* I'd introduce you to him, but Beast isn't really very *sociable* at the moment.

He just broke up with *Storm* a few weeks back and, between you and me, I think all this fuss with *Iceman* leaving has been getting him down a little, *too.*

I *hate* doing these workouts when Cyclops is filling in for Chuck. I bet that snotty, little punk really *gets off* on seeing me jump through all these *hoops* for him.

Oh, *lighten up,* Wolverine. You *had* your chance with Jeannie and you *failed.* Let *Cyclops* have a try. He is a *good guy* with *outstanding,* chiseled cheekbones.

You don't *get* it, Petey. Jeannie and I had been doing this *little dance* for a while... *pretending* we weren't interested and flirting with *other people,* but we *always* knew *the score.*

Please do not hit me with one of those lame *conspiracy theories* about how Xavier is brainwashing *us* like he brain-washed *Magneto.*

If that was the *case,* would Cyclops have left to join *The Brotherhood Of Mutants?* Would I have ever run home to *Russia* in search of a *normal* life?

Yeah, but you all came *running back,* bub.

Don't forget *that* part of the story.

Kitty! What happened?

I *drifted off* for a second and phased through the back of the *stupid car*. Where the heck did we get all this *snow* from *anyway?*

Oops.
Meant to clean that up after *power practice*.

Well, it looks like we have a bright, new *student* starting *first thing* in the *morning*, ladies and gentlemen.

What do you *think*, Jean-- was she as excited about our twenty-four *hour learning program* and quarter of a million *subjects* as she *seemed* to be?

Actually, I think she was a little more excited about our *voluntary classwork* initiative and *Colossus* in his tight, white *T-shirt*, sir.

That said, it's always nice to have an extra pair of hands to help with the *washing up*.

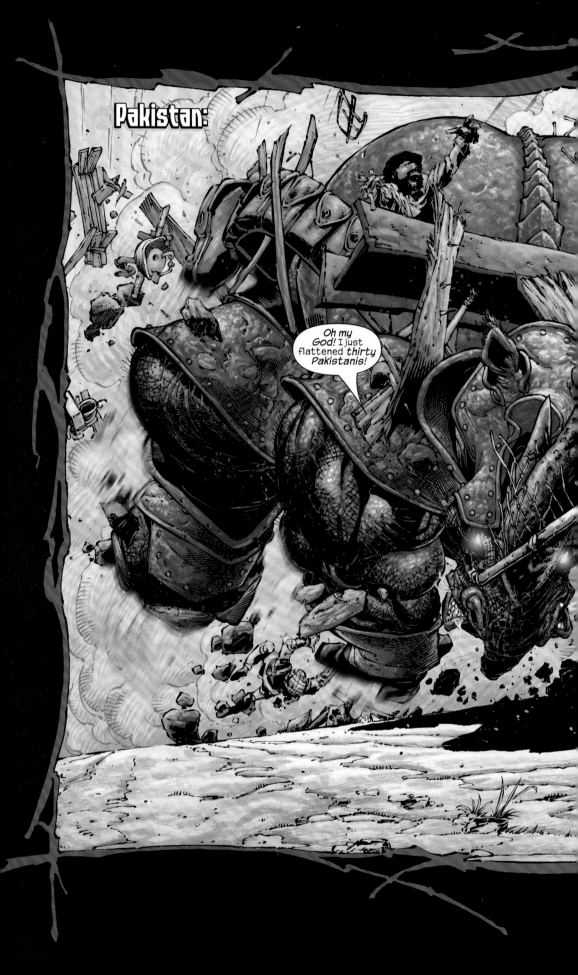

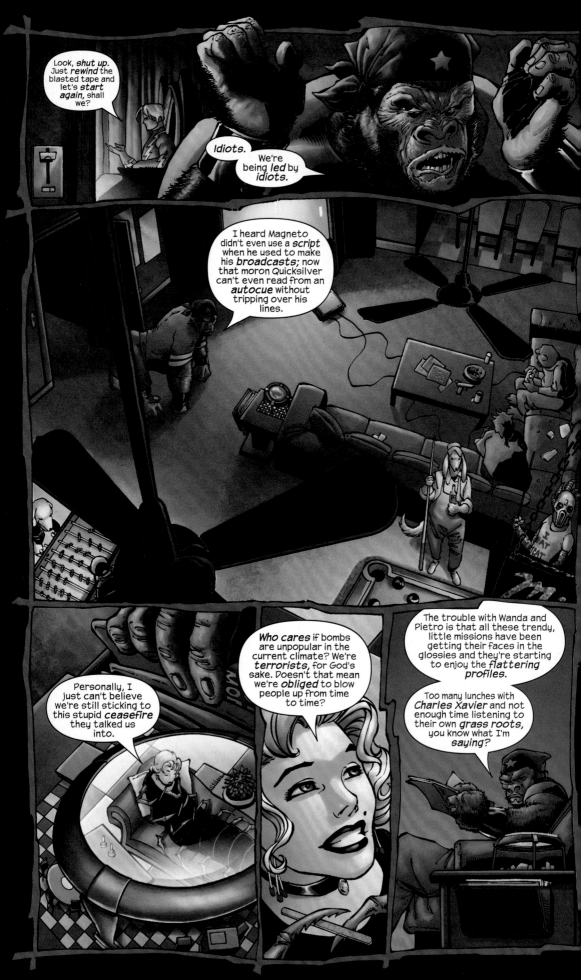

How do you feel about the name *Shadowcat*, Cyclops?

What?

I've been trying to come up with a cool *super hero* name like the ones *you* guys have, but it's really hard not to come off like some crap Saturday morning *cartoon* show.

Do you think Shadowcat sums up my *powers* well enough or do you think I should go for *something else*?

I *think* you should be studying for your physics paper, Kitty.

Tried that and it was *death-by-boredom*, Scotty. What are *you* doing here anyway? Some kind of *geography homework*?

No, Colossus and I might be going on a mission to *The Savage Land* tomorrow morning. I'm just refamiliarizing myself with the *topography* before we leave.

The Savage Land's where *Magneto* used to live, right? I thought the place was some kind of *disaster zone* now. It said on TV nobody's allowed *in or out.*

Yeah, but the *military* have been in there for six months stripping the place apart and looking for anything bright and shiny they might be able to *patent*.

Twenty-four hours ago, the Pentagon lost all *radio communication* and the Professor volunteered to send an *X-team* in to find out what happened.

Sounds cool. You think he'd let *me* tag along?

Not a chance.

C'mon, you've *seen* how good I'm getting with these *phasing-powers*. I was running rings around you guys in the *Danger Room* this morning.

I couldn't care less. Your Mom specifically asked us to restrict your training to *power-control*, Kitty. Missions into *jungle hellholes* are strictly *off limits.*

You scared I'll do an *Iceman* and sue you if you *break* me?

You've had this coming for a *long* time, you cocky little *snot!*

Ditto, meatball!

ISSUE 23

ADAM
KUBERT
ISANOVE

Hey, Henry. We've got our *X-Men* exercises in the *Danger Room* in ten minutes. You *coming?*

Just give me sixty seconds while I finish off this critique of Marx's *Das Kapital*, Kitty. I really feel I have to tighten up my slightly rusty *Russian grammar* here.

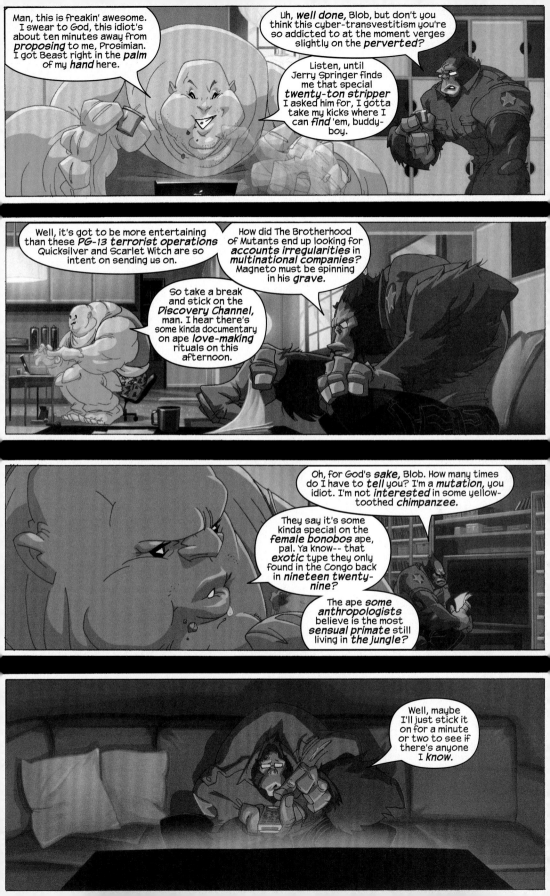

I still can't BELIEVE what happened here last night, Naomi! Cyclops and Wolverine almost KILLED each other over Wolverine's little crush on MARVEL GIRL.

The Professor put them both in a psychic detention room for an hour to settle their differences and now he's sent them off to find some missing U.S. Marines in The Savage Land together!

God, why does Xavier keep sucking up to the establishment like this, Henry? The U.S. Army were only STATIONED in The Savage Land to steal advanced MUTANT TECHNOLOGY.

I realize Cyclops and Wolverine know the area better than anyone, but why risk mutant lives for a species who are openly conspiring AGAINST us?

They aren't ALL against us, Naomi. In fact, our secret sponsors sent a representative this afternoon to see how much money we wanted for this legal battle against Iceman's parents.

I'm really MISSING Bobby right now, you know. I spent all afternoon just sitting in his room listening to that awful CD collection of his.

Poor baby. I wish I'd been there to hold your hand. :(

But what makes you think the X-Men's FINANCIERS are acting out of ALTRUISM, Henry? Isn't their anonymity a sign that Xavier could be controlling their MINDS?

No, they need to remain ANONYMOUS because funding our mission could be devastating to their INTERNATIONAL REPUTATIONS, Naomi.

Ororo and Kitty raised a similar point at a recent TUTORIAL, but I sincerely believe this is one instance where the Professor isn't meddling with ANYONE'S neurons.

Meaning WHAT? That this HELLFIRE CLUB you told me about buys you JUMP-JETS and STATE-OF-THE-ART SECURITY SYSTEMS out of the goodness of their HEARTS? LOL!!!

That's what I LOVE about you, Henry McCoy; your almost child-like belief that human beings AREN'T the most stupid, self-centered species that ever walked the Earth. :)

It's so SWEET!

When the guys at the car plant found out my *son* was in The *X-Men*, I was the first to be laid off in the next wave of *redundancies*.

When your *Mother's* friends found out about you, half of them actually crossed the street to *avoid* her and the other half stopped talking to her *completely*.

There ain't a day *goes by* where someone doesn't vandalize the *porch* or put filth through the *mailbox*, and it's all because our little boy had some bad luck with his *genes*.

This *lawsuit* is the first piece of *good luck* we've had since we found out what was *wrong* with you, Bobby.

This money could mean a *fresh start* in a *whole new place* and it's just *small change* to these billionaires who've been *bankrolling* Xavier.

I hate to put you in this *position*, son, I really *do*...

...but if you don't press ahead with this *compensation claim* for your *injuries*, the three of us are going to be out on the *street* inside six weeks.

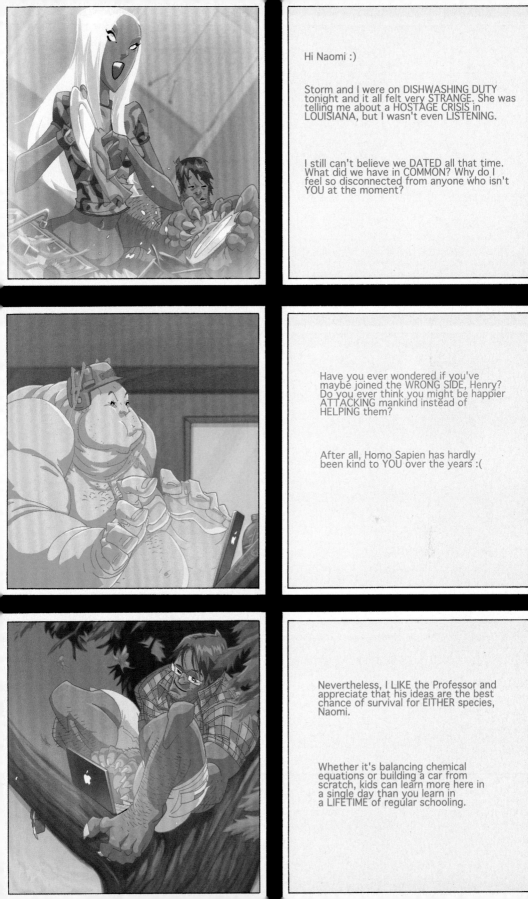

Hi Naomi :)

Storm and I were on DISHWASHING DUTY tonight and it all felt very STRANGE. She was telling me about a HOSTAGE CRISIS in LOUISIANA, but I wasn't even LISTENING.

I still can't believe we DATED all that time. What did we have in COMMON? Why do I feel so disconnected from anyone who isn't YOU at the moment?

Have you ever wondered if you've maybe joined the WRONG SIDE, Henry? Do you ever think you might be happier ATTACKING mankind instead of HELPING them?

After all, Homo Sapien has hardly been kind to YOU over the years :(

Nevertheless, I LIKE the Professor and appreciate that his ideas are the best chance of survival for EITHER species, Naomi.

Whether it's balancing chemical equations or building a car from scratch, kids can learn more here in a single day than you learn in a LIFETIME of regular schooling.

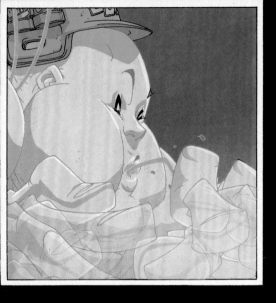

Personally, I just can't understand how an intelligent guy like you can follow the DOCTRINE of that hypocrite.

Where does he get the nerve to write these papers on non-violent solutions to post-human problems when he MURDERED MAGNETO in front of FIVE THOUSAND WITNESSES?

Well, between you and me, that's not exactly how things TRANSPIRED back in Washington, darling.

I'm telling you this in the STRICTEST CONFIDENCE and only because I know I can TRUST you with all my HEART...

...but MAGNETO isn't really DEAD, you know. The whole thing was an ELABORATE RUSE.

The Savage Land:

A vast, Southern Hemisphere land-mass once used as a base by Magneto and his Brotherhood of Mutants.

Well, what's the *verdict*, Wolverine?

The marines are *dead* all right, but it wasn't no *animals* that killed them. The entire troop was taken down before anyone could fire a *shot* and their bodies were *dragged away*.

Direction?

North.

KITTY?!

Oh my God! I just saw a *spider* the size of a *dog* and *freaked out* for a second. I'm totally *sorry*, Wolverine. I'm *cool* now. *Seriously!*

How the heck did *you* get here?

Uh, I hitched a ride in the back of the Blackbird and stayed *intangible* for the whole trip, Cyclops. You know, so Wolverine wouldn't pick up my *scent* or anything?

You *angry*?

No, because you're heading back now to sit in the plane with the *cloaking device* on, Kitty.

Like I said, your Mom made it clear she didn't *want* you on these missions and, quite frankly, we're all a little *scared* of her.

Oh, c'mon, Scott. I won't tell her if *you* don't...

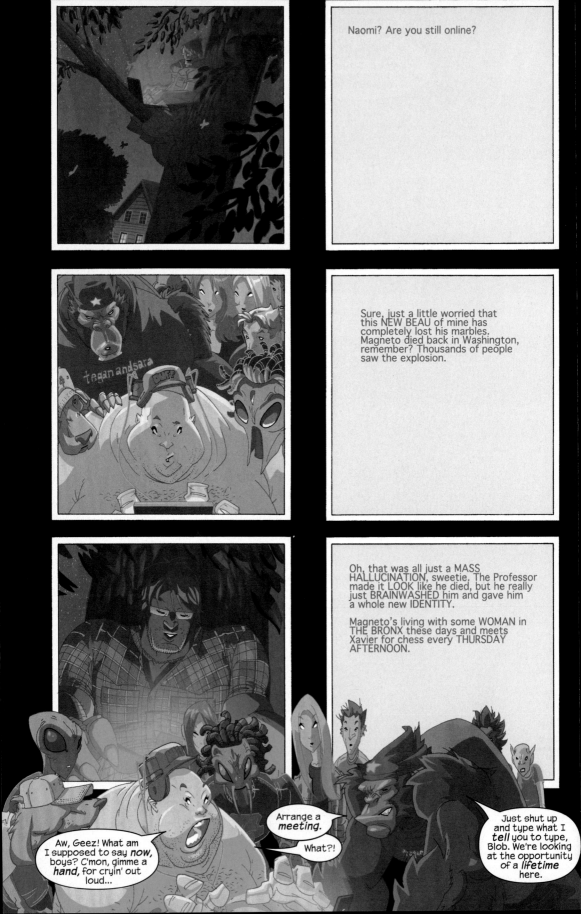

Naomi? Are you still online?

Sure, just a little worried that this NEW BEAU of mine has completely lost his marbles. Magneto died back in Washington, remember? Thousands of people saw the explosion.

Oh, that was all just a MASS HALLUCINATION, sweetie. The Professor made it LOOK like he died, but he really just BRAINWASHED him and gave him a whole new IDENTITY.

Magneto's living with some WOMAN in THE BRONX these days and meets Xavier for chess every THURSDAY AFTERNOON.

Aw, Geez! What am I supposed to say *now*, boys? C'mon, gimme a *hand*, for cryin' out loud...

Arrange a *meeting*.

What?!

Just shut up and type what I *tell* you to type, Blob. We're looking at the opportunity of a *lifetime* here.

LISTEN, Henry. I've really got to log-off in a second, but I've been thinking about what you SAID earlier and you're RIGHT.

It's CRAZY not to meet up when we obviously feel so close to each other. Why don't we meet up tomorrow and see how it GOES? Even if it's just for a COFFEE...

C'mon, c'mon. I thought you were supposed to be *lonely,* you ugly, blue freak...

Sounds TERRIFIC, Naomi.

Where do you want to MEET?

Beautiful.

ISSUE 24

ADAM KUBERT
ISANOVE

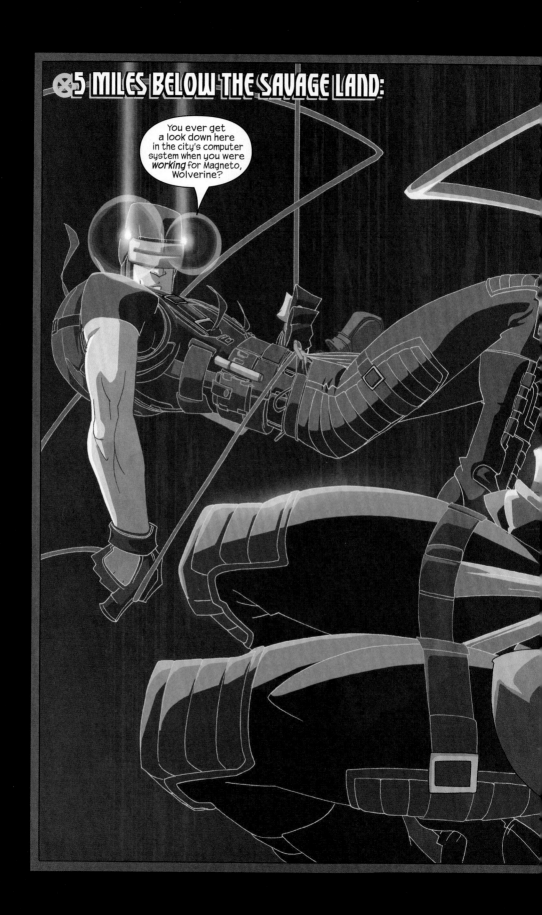

Oh, *come on*, Professor. I'm hardly going to *sue* you.

Besides, a hundred million dollars isn't even *lunch money* to those super-rich *Hellfire Club* guys you said were *funding* this little enterprise.

Kitty? I'm losing your *signal* and my telepathy doesn't *stretch* to the Southern Hemisphere. Just tell me *quickly*-- do you want Peter to come down and *pick you up* or *not*?

Professor, I can turn *intangible* at the drop of a hat and I'm sitting on the roof of a billion dollar *warplane.* I hardly think I'm going to get *mugged.*

Teenagers! How are *you* feeling today, Jean? *Better?*

Yeah. *much* better.

I *told* you it would pass, Jean. Your powers are just expanding as your body *blossoms* into *adulthood.* Almost exactly the same thing happened to *me* when I was your age, you know.

Last night I actually managed a *full night's sleep* without a *single interruption.*

No *bad dreams*, no *hallucinations*, no Egyptian *Phoenix gods* telling me they were coming here to *eat the world...*

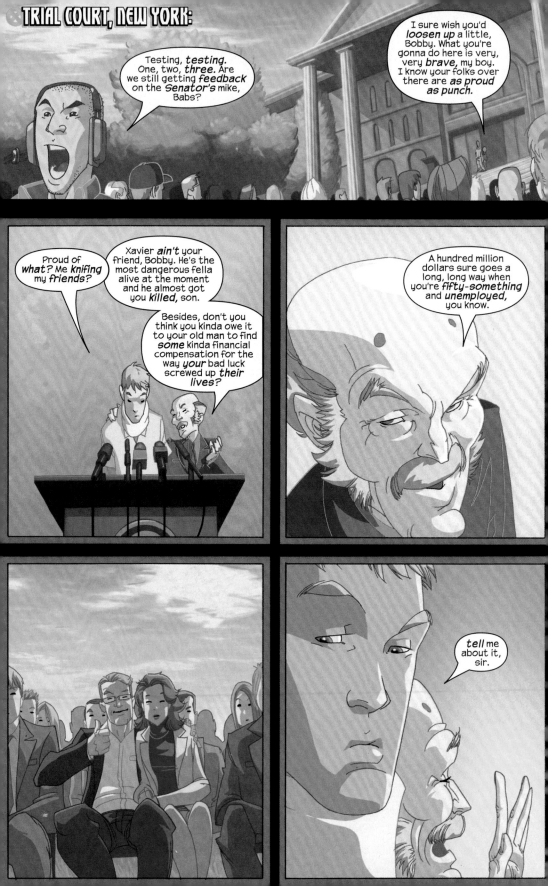

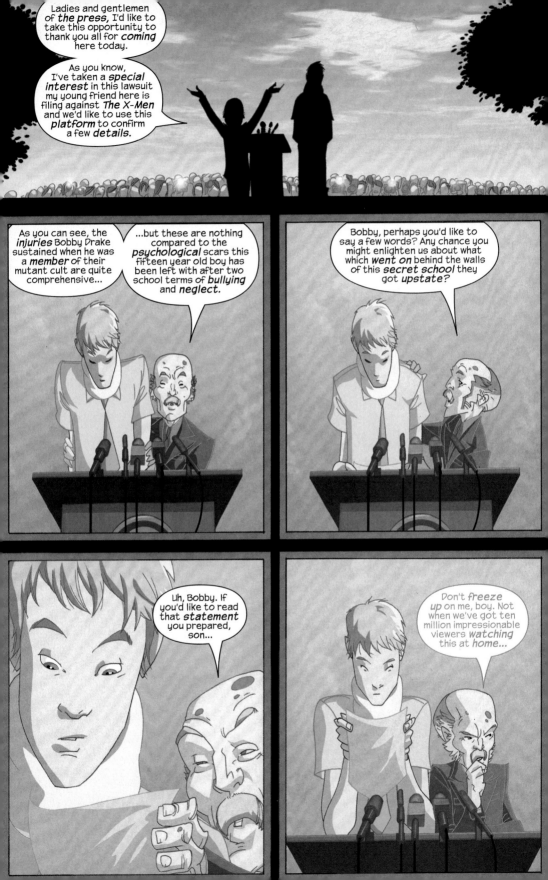

Hey.

I got a *speech* here in front of me, just like Senator Turk has, but I'm not gonna *read* it 'coz, well, I didn't really *write* it and just about *none* of this stuff is true *anyway*.

What?

Sure, Professor Xavier sent us on *dangerous missions*, but it was only ever to help *ordinary people* like *you*.

Sure, some of us almost got *killed* a few times, but he's training us to be *super heroes*, for God's sake. A few broken bones is kinda *par for the course*, right?

I know my Mom and Dad could really use that *money* right now. I know I've really screwed up their *lives* and I feel really, really *bad* about it, but I'm not gonna sit up here and *lie*.

I'm not gonna *bleed* some guy just because he's *rich* and help some stupid senator close down a *school* teaching ideas that *scare* him. I got too much *integrity* for that...

...and I learned that lesson at *Xavier's*.

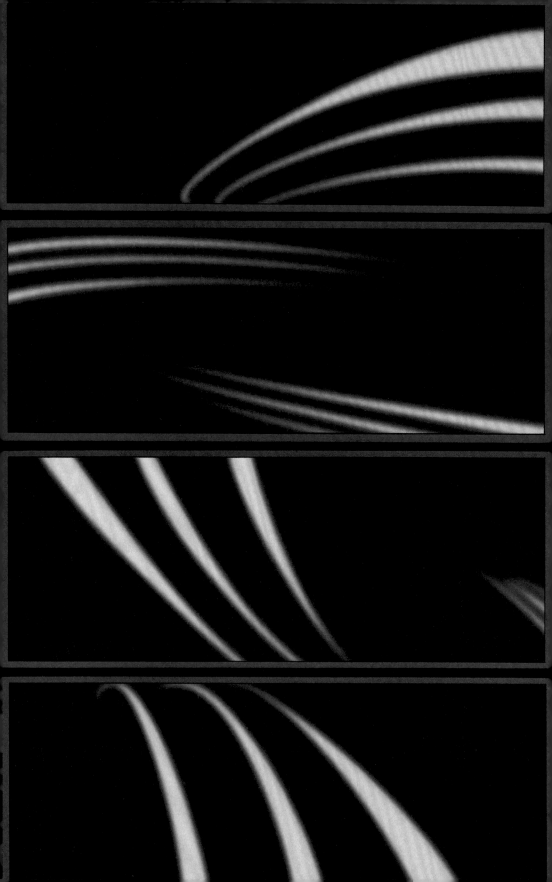

Uh, have we *met?*

Oh, you *disappoint* me. After all, I can remember everything about *you,* right down to the most insignificant *detail.*

You, Wolverine, as you lay on your bed after killing the head of that *corporation*-- ordering me to increase the air-conditioning until you couldn't feel your *hands* anymore.

You, Cyclops, after *shunning* the advances of *Scarlet Witch,* surfing through my *cable channels* for something quite *exotic.*

Are you really telling me that you don't recognize the *digital mind* that worked the *lights,* the *circuit boards,* the *defenses* and the *air-conditioning* five miles up?

No freakin' way...

That's right, Wolverine. I'm the computer that used to keep *Magneto's* perfect city *running* on time.

If you'd allow me to escort you to the *wheelchair ramp* around *the corner*, Professor Xavier...

No, no. I've waited *far too long* for this to enter *The Hellfire Club* by anything other than your grand *front entrance*, young man.

I might not boast *telekinetic skills* on *Marvel Girl's* scale, but I'm more than capable of levitating *this* little contraption.

You really sure you're *up* to this, Jean?

To be honest, I'm the best I've been in *weeks*, Ororo. If I seem a little *distracted*, it's just that I'm worried about *Scott* going off on this *Savage Land* thing.

I hate having him outside my *telepathic range* like this-- especially when the psoriasis on my *elbows* is flaring up.

Nine times out of *ten*, that means somebody I *care* about is *suffering* out there.

You sure you don't wanna just *bail*?

Oh, no. We couldn't *do* that to the Professor. He's been as *giddy* as a *schoolgirl* since these guys said they wanted to meet him.

Besides, what's the worst that can *happen*?

A word in your ear, Mister Rasputin, but I have it on very good authority that Mister *Marts* and Mister *Raicht* over there would be *very* happy to *meet* you, sir.

Would you like me to handle the *introductions?*

I'm *flattered,* Professor. And *honored,* of course. It's a delight to finally *meet* you in *the flesh,* sir.

Mister Shaw, I don't know where to *begin.* Suffice to say, if it wasn't for *you* and your generous *associates* here, there wouldn't even *be* an X-Men.

Greenspan? No, *sorry.* Doesn't ring any *bells,* man. You ain't that old guy that used to be the boss on *Charlie's Angels,* are you?

I think my students are a little *star-struck* by your *guests* tonight, Mister Seville.

To be honest, I think our *membership* are just as excited about meeting *them,* Professor Xavier.

Mister Shaw, the Hellfire Club's *current* grandmaster, has spoken of *little else* lately.

Sebastian Shaw? From *Shaw* Industries?

None other.

Just investing in *the future*, Charles. The Hellfire Club is *quite adept* at picking winners, you know, and there's no *safer bet* right now than *homo-sapiens superior.*

But *coming out* like this before the *world's press* and telling everyone that the club has been funding my *ideas.* It's such a *bold move.*

Merely time to take a *stand*, Charles.

You and your brother mutants shall inherit the *earth* some day and, quite frankly, it's in *everyone's* best interests to make this transition as *peaceful* as possible.

I believe we must teach the public that the *alternative* is just too painful to even *contemplate.*

Champagne, gentlemen?

Well, normally, I *don't*, but seeing as this is such a *special occasion...*

To *the future*, Charles, and whatever surprises it might have in *store* for us.

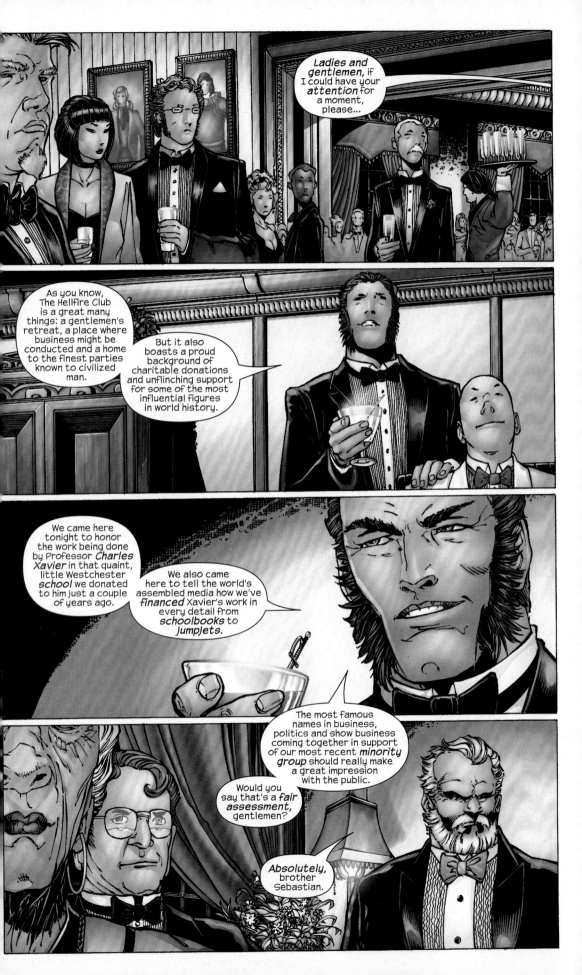

Ladies and gentlemen, if I could have your *attention* for a moment, please...

As you know, The Hellfire Club is a great many things: a gentlemen's retreat, a place where business might be conducted and a home to the finest parties known to civilized man.

But it also boasts a proud background of charitable donations and unflinching support for some of the most influential figures in world history.

We came here tonight to honor the work being done by Professor *Charles Xavier* in that quaint, little Westchester *school* we donated to him just a couple of years ago.

We also came here to tell the world's assembled media how we've *financed* Xavier's work in every detail from *schoolbooks* to *jumpjets.*

The most famous names in business, politics and show business coming together in support of our most recent *minority group* should really make a great impression with the public.

Would you say that's a *fair assessment,* gentlemen?

Absolutely, brother Sebastian.

Sir? Are you *all right?*

Fine, Blob. Absolutely *fine*. Just a little *lightheaded* from the *psychic deprogramming.*

Give me a moment to *recollect* my *thoughts* again and *appreciate* who I *am.*

Who *did* this, incidentally?

Who among you had the courage to go behind my children's backs and *arrange* this little rescue? To *whom* do I owe my *thanks* here?

Actually, I believe that would be *me*, Magneto.

Prosimian, sir-- one of the several super-evolved *primates* who were freed from a lab on a Brotherhood *anti-vivisection mission.*

It was *me* who hatched the little scheme to find out where you were. It was *my* idea and *mine alone.*

And *you* are?

Well, it seems I am forever in your *debt*, Prosimian. What you organized here shows tremendous *forethought* and considerable *bravery...*

Issue #21
Cover Process
by ADAM KUBERT

Issue #22
Cover Process
by ADAM KUBERT

Issue #23
Cover Process
by ADAM KUBERT

ULTIMATE X-MEN #23 COVER SKETCH
(BRICK WALL TYPE BACKGROUND)